a cat and a puppy

the puppy on
the log

a puppy

a dog and a
puppy

the puppy in
the mud

the puppy in the
pond

the frog and the
puppy in the pond

the cat and the
dog and the puppy

Mid-Winter Warn
2022

Charlie Ellingworth

Three o'clock is always too late, or too early, for anything you want to do.
Jean-Paul Sartre

The ultimate aim of the poet should be to touch our heart by showing his own.
Thomas Hardy

I've polled 1,000 women asking if they would sleep with Boris. Twenty per cent said: 'Never again'.
The pollster Frank Luntz, a university contemporary of Johnson

The best thing about the future is that it comes one day at a time.
Lincoln

I have a foreboding of an America in my children's or my grandchildren's time — when the United States is a service and information economy; when nearly all the key manufacturing industries have slipped away to other countries; when awesome technological powers are in the hands of a very few, and no one representing the public interest can even grasp the issues; when the people have lost the ability to set their own agendas or knowledgeably question those in authority; when, clutching our crystals and nervously consulting our horoscopes, our critical faculties in decline, unable to distinguish between what feels good and what's true we slide, almost without noticing, back into superstition and darkness. The dumbing down of America is most evident in the slow decay of substantive content in the enormously-influential media, the 30-second sound bites (now down to 10 seconds or less), lowest common denominator programming, credulous presentations on pseudoscience and superstition, but especially a kind of celebration of ignorance.
Carl Sagan, The Demon-Haunted World (1995)

Virginity of soul and impurity of body can go together.
Van Gogh

To be amiable in society, one must allow oneself to be told what one already knows.
Talleyrand

A nation is a group of people united by a mistaken view about the past and a hatred of their neighbours.
Ernest Renan, French Historian

Temper is what gets most of us into trouble. Pride is what keeps us there.
Mark Twain

The secret of longevity is bannisters.
Michael Bloomberg

All human beings have three lives: public, private, and secret.
Gabriel Garcia Marquez

The opposite of a correct statement is a false statement. But the opposite of a profound truth may well be another profound truth.
Niels Bohr

You don't have to burn books to destroy a culture. Just get people to stop reading them.
Ray Bradbury

Each historical epoch has been characterised by a set of interlocking explanations of reality and social, political, and economic arrangements based on them. The classical world, Middle Ages, Renaissance, and modern world all cultivated their concepts of the individual and society, theorising about where and how each fits into the enduring order of things. When prevailing understandings no longer sufficed to explain perceptions of reality—events experienced, discoveries made, other cultures encountered— revolutions in thought (and sometimes in politics) occurred, and a new epoch was born. The emerging AI age is increasingly posing epochal challenges to today's concept of reality.

Scientific revolutions, especially in the twentieth century, have evolved technology and philosophy, but the central Enlightenment premise of a knowable world being unearthed, step-by-step, by human minds has persisted. Until now...

As we are growing increasingly dependent on digital augmentation, we are entering a new epoch in which the reasoning human mind is yielding its pride of place as the sole discoverer, knower, and cataloguer of the world's phenomena. While the technological achievements of the age of reason have been significant, until recently they had remained sporadic enough to be reconciled with tradition... But we have reached a tipping point: we can no longer conceive of some of our innovations as extensions of that which we already know...the revolution of digitisation and the advancement of AI have produced phenomena that are truly new, not simply more powerful or efficient versions of things past...

The digital world has little patience for wisdom; its values are shaped by approbation, not introspection. It inherently challenges the Enlightenment proposition that reason is the most important element of consciousness.

The AI age needs its own Descartes, its own Kant, to explain what is being created and what it will mean for humanity...The governance of people is guided by an ethic. AI begs for an ethic of its own...The challenge is compounded by the difficulty of designing effective verification regimes for a technology that is ethereal, opaque and easily distributed... Morality, volition, even causality do not map neatly onto a world of anonymous AI.

Henry Kissinger and Eric Schmidt: The Age of AI and our Human Future

3

Film music should have the same relationship to the film drama as somebody's piano playing in my living room has on the book I am reading.
Stravinsky

Why do people not talk about their war experiences? Because, if they're honest with themselves, they know they were just bleeding terrified a lot of the time. They're absolutely at the edge of keeping control over themselves and losing control over themselves. You just don't like that feeling. You also don't like the thought that if your government puts a gun into your hands and says 'Go to it', you do. You recognise sadistic instincts. You recognise how wafer-thin is the veneer of civilisation.
Sir Christopher Hogg, an impressive captain of industry who died this year, on his National Service experience.

There are no such things as foreign lands; only foreign travellers.
Robert Louis Stevenson.

Terence attributed to it a Suez-like significance in the nation's alimentary canal.
Stephen Bayley on Terence Conran's first restaurant, The Soup Kitchen

Men can only be highly civilised when other men, inevitably less civilised, are there to guard and feed them them.
George Orwell

For the America that I was travelling through had changed its character in thirty years. It remained (in the 70s) the biggest of all the nations, and in my judgement still in many ways the best, but it had somehow lost its grandeur. To the world at large it no longer represented all that was hopeful and generous in human affairs; to itself, I felt, it presented an uncertain image. Gone was that wonderfully seductive

4

confidence, gone the certainty that what was good for America was good for mankind. The endearing youthful swagger had become a paunchy strut. Hubris was in the air too, and with it a touch of unwitting pathos, for by definition hubris portends humiliation.
Jan Morris: Allegorizing

I'm optimistic about life. If I can be optimistic when I'm nearly dead, surely the rest of you can handle a little inflation.
Charlie Munger, Warren Buffett's partner - who is 98.

If you are thin, people will wonder why you bother to watch what you eat. Therein lies a warning about our species' ability to take any sort of preventive action, whether against climate change or viral pandemics.
Janan Ganesh

The past is terrible, the present catastrophic; thank God we don't have a future.
Armenian Proverb

What Orwell feared was that there would those who would ban books. What Huxley feared was that there would be no

reason to ban a book, because there would be no one who wanted to read one.
Neil Postman: Amusing ourselves to death

History is the sum total of the things that could have been avoided.
Konrad Adenauer

History is the memory of states.
Henry Kissinger

Cancel culture - that dismal oxymoron.
The Economist

The world is full of fools and faint hearts; and yet everyone has courage enough to bear the misfortunes, and wisdom enough to manage the affairs, of his neighbour.
Benjamin Franklin

He was good in the box, then he was good on the box, now he's in a box.
Gary Lineker: on his own obituary

A man may be a fool and not know it, but not if he is married.
H.L. Mencken

It is not a lack of love, but a lack of friendship that makes unhappy marriages.
Neitzsche

Having more money doesn't make you happier. I have 50 million dollars but I'm just as happy as when I had 48 million.
Arnold Schwarzenegger.

And then, just yesterday, when I was talking about the Carr case to my dentist (when Jimmy Carr had made a holocaust joke that went down very badly) he said to me: "The thing to remember is that Hitler killed six million Jews and one milkman."

"A milkman?" I said.

"You see," he replied. "Nobody cares about the Jews."
Giles Coren

As one grows older, one becomes wiser and more foolish.
François de La Rochefoucauld

Part of the genius of the ancient laws, by which the Spartan polity had maintained herself intact over six centuries, was the leavening of youth with age throughout all institutions. There were veterans everywhere; no club or clique escaped supervision by its elders.
Steven Pressfield

There are three times when you should never say anything important to a person: when he is tired, when he is angry, and when he has just made a mistake.
David Phillips

The mob's going to want a chicken to kill and they won't care much who it is. Why don't people look at mobs not as men, but as mobs? A mob nearly always seems to act reasonably, for a mob.
John Steinbeck

Whenever you find yourself on the side of the majority, it is time to pause and reflect.
Mark Twain

The future is certain, it's the past that's unpredictable.
Old Soviet Joke

How can we know the dancer from the dance?
WB Yeats

Death took away an era soaked in evil, leaving us only with the habit of clinging ignobly to life.
Ai Weiwei on the death of Mao

Mr Speaker, I said the honourable member was a liar it is true and I am sorry for it. The honourable member may place the punctuation where he pleases.
Richard Brinsley Sheridan

Time I spend on Netflix is time I don't spend challenging myself to listen to new music or watch a film that might broaden my horizons; it's time I spend watching something that isn't good enough for me to recommend it to anyone else, but isn't bad enough for me to get up and do something better.
Stephen Bush

I don't like that man, I must get to know him better.
Lincoln

Hillary Clinton is America's ex-wife.
PJ O'Rourke

When fishes flew and forests walked
  And figs grew upon thorn,
Some moment when the moon was blood
  Then surely I was born.
 With monstrous head and sickening cry
  And ears like errant wings,
The devil's walking parody
  On all four-footed things.

The tattered outlaw of the earth,
  Of ancient crooked will;
Starve, scourge, deride me: I am dumb,
  I keep my secret still.

Fools! For I also had my hour;

One far fierce hour and sweet:
There was a shout about my ears,
   And palms before my feet.

GK Chesterton: The Donkey

Everyone complains of his memory, but no one complains
of his judgment.
de La Rochefoucauld

*This is from Wikipedia about the Ultra-massive Black Hole
called Ton 618 that is bigger than ALL the stars in our
galaxy, The Milky Way.*

As a quasar, Ton 618 is believed to be the active galactic
nucleus at the centre of a galaxy, the engine of which is a
supermassive black hole feeding on intensely hot gas and
matter in an accretion disc. The light originating from the
quasar is estimated to be 10.8 billion years old. Due to the
brilliance of the central quasar, the surrounding galaxy is
outshined by it and hence is not visible from Earth. It shines
as brilliantly as 140 trillion times that of the Sun, making it
one of the brightest objects in the known Universe.
The mass of the central black hole of Ton 618 is at least 66
billion solar masses. This is considered one of the highest
masses ever recorded for such an object; higher than the
mass of all stars in the Milky Way galaxy combined, which
is 64 billion solar masses and 15,300 times more massive
than Sagittarius A, the Milky Way's central black hole.
With such high mass, Ton 618 may fall into a proposed new
classification of ultra-massive black hole. A black hole of
this mass is about 390 billion km in diameter which is more
than 40 times the distance from Neptune to the Sun. To give
that perspective, Earth is 146m kilometres from the Sun
and Neptune 4,474m kilometres.

We often refuse to accept an idea merely because the tone of voice in which it has been expressed is unsympathetic to us.
Nietzsche

Always read something that will make you look good if you die in the middle of it.
PJ O'Rourke

For us, there is only the trying. The rest is not our business.
TS Eliot

There is only one basic human right, the right to do as you damn well please. And with it comes the only basic human duty, the duty to take the consequences.
PJ O'Rourke

I've reluctantly discarded the notion of my continuing to manage the portfolio after my death—abandoning my hope to give new meaning to the term "thinking outside the box."
Warren Buffett

Quantity has a quality all of its own.
Stalin

A pessimist sees the difficulty in every opportunity; an optimist sees the opportunity in every difficulty.
Churchill

Truth came to market but could not be sold; however, we buy lies with ready cash.
West African saying

I do not want my picture in your offices: the President is not an icon, an idol or a portrait. Hang your kids 'photos instead, and look at them each time you are making a decision.
From Volodymyr Zelensky's inaugural address 2019

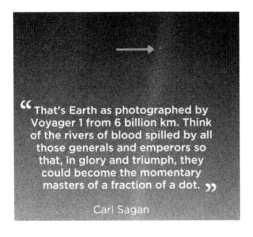

> **"** That's Earth as photographed by Voyager 1 from 6 billion km. Think of the rivers of blood spilled by all those generals and emperors so that, in glory and triumph, they could become the momentary masters of a fraction of a dot. **"**
>
> Carl Sagan

If nobody can learn from the past, then there's no point in raking it up.
Billie Holiday

The bigger the dog, the bigger the crap.
Ukrainian proverb

God has always been hard on the poor.
Jean-Paul Marat
This is from CS Lewis's sermon in Oxford's University Church on the outbreak of war in 1939.

The war creates no absolutely new situation: it simply aggravates the permanent human situation so that we can no longer ignore it. Human life has always been lived on the edge of a precipice. Human culture has always had to exist under the shadow of something infinitely more important than itself. If men had postponed the search for knowledge and beauty until they were secure, the search would never have begun.
We are mistaken when we compare war with "normal life". Life has never been normal. Even those periods which we think most tranquil, like the nineteenth century, turn out, on closer inspection, to be full of cries, alarms, difficulties, emergencies. Plausible reasons have never been lacking for putting off all

11

merely cultural activities until some imminent danger has been averted or some crying injustice put right. But humanity long ago chose to neglect those plausible reasons. They wanted knowledge and beauty now, and would not wait for the suitable moment that would never come. Periclean Athens leaves us not only the Parthenon but, significantly, the Funeral Oration.

The insects have chosen a different line: they have sought first the material welfare and security of the hive, and presumable they have their reward. Men are different. They propound mathematical theorems in beleaguered cities, conduct metaphysical arguments in condemned cells, make jokes on scaffold, discuss the last new poem while advancing to the walls of Quebec, and comb their hair at Thermopylae. This is not panache; it is our nature.

When my arms wrap you round I press
My heart upon the loveliness
That has long faded from the world.
WB Yeats: He Remembers Forgotten Beauty

The right word may be effective, but no word was ever as effective as a rightly timed pause.
Mark Twain

The first time I see a jogger smiling, I'll consider it.
Joan Rivers

A creator is not in advance of his generation but he is the first of his contemporaries to be conscious of what is happening to his generation.
Gertrude Stein: Picasso

The scientists of today think deeply instead of clearly. One must be sane to think clearly, but one can think deeply and be quite insane.
Nikola Tesla

I look into my glass,
  And view my wasting skin,
And say, "Would God it came to pass
  My heart had shrunk as thin!"

For then, I, undistrest
  By hearts grown cold to me,
Could lonely wait my endless rest
  With equanimity.

But Time, to make me grieve,
  Part steals, lets part abide;
And shakes this fragile frame at eve
  With throbbings of noontide.

Thomas Hardy: I Look into my Glass

To be ignorant of what occurred before you were born is to remain always a child.
Cicero

Civilisation is the lamb's skin in which barbarism masquerades.
Thomas Bailey Aldrich

You can tell more about a person by what he says about others than you can by what others say about him.
Leo Aikman
It is easier to forgive an enemy than to forgive a friend.
William Blake

Ability is of little account without opportunity.
Napoleon

Children have never been very good at listening to their elders, but they've never failed to imitate them.
James Baldwin

From The Times Births, Marriages and Deaths
MORISON Thomas Richard Atkin "snuffed it" on 19th March, aged 83. No funeral; no memorial; no mourning; no flowers; no worries. Grateful thanks to the cancer team at the neurological-oncology centre, Southampton. With huge thanks to my wonderful wife for caring for me so well; to my wonderful children: thank you especially for giving me four beautiful and talented granddaughters. And thanks to my furry four-footed friend, Dave: sorry I was not a better walker for you at the end. Just perhaps, see you all later..."

This is from The Matter with Things by Iain Macgilchrist - an elegant description of the functioning of the Left and Right hemispheres of the brain.

The Left Hand aims to narrow things down to a certainty, while the Right Hand opens them up into possibility. The Right Hand is able to sustain ambiguity and the holding together of information that appears to have contrary implications, without having to make an 'either/or 'decision, and to collapse it, as the Left Hand tends to do, in favour of one of them.

The left hemisphere's limited appreciation of depth in space and time is in keeping with its tendency towards stasis. It seems to lack appreciation, not just of motion, but of emotion; it relatively lacks appropriate emotional depth, or concern, tending to be irritable or facetious, especially when challenged. It tends to disown problems, and pass the responsibility to others; is overconfident about what it cannot in the nature of things know much about; fabricates (often improbable) stories to cover its ignorance; sees parts at the expense of wholes; tends to see 'from the outside', rather than experience 'from the inside'; and has an affinity for the inanimate, and for tools and machines in particular. It is also quite confident it is right.

He has mastered the use of error, omission, exaggeration, diminution, equivocation and flat denial. He has perfected casuistry, circumlocution, false equivalence and false analogy.

He is equally adept at the ironic jest, the fib and the grand lie; the weasel word and the half-truth; the hyperbolic lie, the obvious lie, and the bullshit lie – which may inadvertently be true.
Rory Stewart on Boris Johnson

Every advance in communication technology makes it slightly harder to talk to the person you want to in a big company.
Rod Liddle

Success breeds a disregard for the possibility of failure.
Hyman Minsky

Everything before the 'but 'is bullshit.
Westminster saying

The sad truth of the matter is that most evil is done by people who never made up their minds to be or do either evil or good.
Hannah Arendt

In no nation are the fruits of accomplishment more secure... I have no fears for the future of our country. It is bright with hope.
Herbert Hoover, Inaugural Address, March 4, 1929

In every major economic downturn in U.S. history, the villains have been the heroes during the preceding boom.
Peter Drucker

The modern world is said to over-reward academic intelligence, and so it does. Of the most successful people I know, though, none are the very smartest in their organisations, much less their generational cohorts. Beyond a certain cognitive level, another trait seems to become more decisive. 'Optimism' is the crispest word for it, but it gives a banal ring to what is a complex mental gift: the sifting for good news among the bad, the reinterpretation of adverse events as what one had wanted all along. It can border on self-deception. But it also gets people through the night. And the most underrated component of success is continuing to show up.

Janan Ganesh in the FT

The world is ruled by letting things take their course.
Lao-Tzu

The whole map of Europe has been changed…but as the deluge subsides and the waters fall short we see the dreary steeples of Fermanagh and Tyrone emerging once again.
Churchill, after the First World War, on the perennial stubbornness of the Irish Question

Nothing is particularly hard if you divide it into small jobs.
Henry Ford

"Dad, you've got the camera upside down"

Sometimes I wonder if the world is being run by smart people who are putting us on or by imbeciles who really mean it.
Mark Twain

On another occasion we visited Jeffrey Archer in his penthouse apartment overlooking the Thames. Once he had proudly showed us his Monet, his wife, Mary offered us coffee. It was strange, and curiously poignant, to learn that after decades of marriage she had to check if her husband took sugar.
Rachel Sylvester

I cannot teach anybody anything. I can only make them think.
Socrates

Asparagus is not a vegetable to be eaten on one's own. It is to be eaten *a deux*, either with someone you are in the habit of sleeping with or someone you hope to be sleeping with very soon. To eat it alone, or to admit to eating it alone, is, I sometimes think, more shameful than to admit to masturbation. All my happiest memories of the asparagus season have involved eating it with women I have loved. And it doesn't even have to be picked up by the fingers. I once made, for my beloved H, a dish of asparagus tips in scrambled eggs (the eggs stirred over the

17

lowest possible heat for half an hour (with a few twists of black pepper and a restaurant secret here - a few shavings of Parmesan). After her first mouthful she said "Marry me", and I should have.
Nicholas Lezard in the New Statesman

"Nothing personal, Mr Knight, but I was hoping to speak to one of the others."

It is lack of confidence, more than anything else, that kills a civilisation. We can destroy ourselves by cynicism and disillusion, just effectively as by bombs.
Kenneth Clark: Civilisation

Freedom (n.): To ask nothing. To expect nothing. To depend on nothing.
Ayn Ran

The trouble with compiling this compendium of hideous grammar is that every day seemingly brings another inane and infuriating neologism. For example, last week I heard a journalist — a British journalist — use the phrase "lean into the narrative". What the hell does that even mean? Incidentally, "narrative" is another grossly overused word. I'm not sure why

it is used at all. We've been served perfectly well by "lie" for centuries.
Rod Liddle

The greatest assembly of intelligence ever? Participants of the 5th Solvay Conference on Quantum Mechanics, 1927. 17 of the 29 attendees were or became Nobel Prize winners.

Back: Auguste Piccard, Emile Henriot, Paul Ehrenfest, Edouard Herzen, Theophile de Donder, Erwin Schrodinger, JE Verschaffelt, Wolfgang Pauli, Werner Heisenberg, Ralph Fowler, Lean Brillouin.

Middle: Peter Debye, Martin Knudsen, William Lawrence Bragg, Hendrik Anthony Kramers, Paul Dirac, Arthur Compton, Louis de Broglie, Max Born, Niels Bohr.

Front: Irving Langmuir, Max Planck, Marie Curie, Hendrik Lorentz, Albert Einstein, Paul Langevin, Charles-Eugene Guye, CTR Wilson, Owen Richardson.

Thinking is more interesting than knowing, but not than looking.
Goethe

What is woke culture if not the howl of a generation of underemployed humanities graduates?
Janan Ganesh

I do not fear death. I have been dead for billions and billions of years before I was born and had not suffered the slightest inconvenience from it.
Mark Twain
Keep death daily before your eyes.
St Benedict

Most actions that the Roman government took in response to crises—such as debasing the currency, raising taxes, expanding the army, and conscripting labor—were practical solutions to immediate problems. It would have been unthinkable not to adopt such measures. Cumulatively, however, these practical steps made the empire ever weaker.
Joseph Tainter, on the decline of the Roman Empire

GP shortages

It is better for a leader to make a mistake in forgiving than to make a mistake in punishing.
Muhammad

The nice thing about egotists is that they don't talk about other people.
Lucille S. Harper

I have never been able to find out precisely what feminism is; I only know that people call me a feminist whenever I express sentiments that differentiate me from a doormat.
Rebecca West

Glory be to God for dappled things –
    For skies of couple-colour as a brinded cow;
For rose-moles all in stipple upon trout that swim;
Fresh-firecoal chestnut-falls; finches 'wings;
    Landscape plotted and pieced – fold, fallow, and plough;
    And áll trádes, their gear and tackle and trim.
    All things counter, original, spare, strange;
        Whatever is fickle, freckled (who knows how?)
With swift, slow; sweet, sour; adazzle, dim;
He fathers-forth whose beauty is past change:
        Praise him.

Gerard Manley Hopkins: Pied Beauty

'Boris's Ethics Advisor 'sounds like something you'd have printed on a T-shirt for a stag do.
Grainne Maguire

One measure of leadership is the calibre of people who choose to follow you.
Dennis Peer

Wisdom is founded on memory; happiness on forgetfulness.
Mason Cooley

Dogs come when they're called; cats take a message and get back to you.
Mary Bly

After our gin he climbed back on his mini-tractor and, accompanied by one of the cats, I went for a short walk as far as the moat. In it was a foot of water already, and two excited frogs, agile as spiders, loud as donkeys, were scaling the interior wall. I sat on the wall and the cat jumped up on to my lap. I was wearing shorts and sandals. I looked down at my wasted calves and visible shinbones and further down at my blackened toenails and regarded it all with fresh incredulity. And even here, beside the River Lot in the merry month of May, I envied the frogs and the cat and the screaming, swooping swallows and even the two surprised goldfish the fullness of their unheeding lives.
Jeremy Clarke in the Spectator. His descriptions of his cancer treatment in France are both moving and lyrical

This is why I invite people to ponder the question: is the money we earn straightforwardly ours? I ask this having looked at a website recently and noted that my salary places me within the top 1 per cent of earners. This came as a surprise because my income has risen so gradually over the years that I have never "felt" rich. I still think of myself — as I guess most people do — according to where I grew up: comprehensive school, dad battling to rise up the civil service, mum stacking shelves at Asda.
And yet, having been fortunate to do well financially, I can say one thing with conviction: the money doesn't feel like "mine" in any straightforward sense. When I look at the arc of my "success", I do not see "my" work ethic or "my" talent but the

myriad contributions of others — and I don't just mean my
wonderful parents. I think of Brian Cowan, a primary school
teacher, who died of cancer before I could track him down and
tell him how his kindness and brilliance changed my life. I think
of Peter Charters, who started a table-tennis club and turned it
into a hive of activity. He worked every afternoon as a volunteer
and today, in his seventies, is still going.
And yet this barely scratches the surface of the social context of
"my" success. Consider those who fell during wars to protect our
freedoms, the pioneers who built our institutions, the forgotten
sacrifices of millions, the totality of which put backbone in that
abstraction we call society. I do not see "my" money or "my"
fortune but an intricate ecosystem without which none of us
could survive, still less flourish.
Matthew Syed

The qualities Boris possesses, and which allowed him to reach
the top of his profession, also sowed the seeds of his eventual
downfall. The gods gave him brains, geniality, boundless self-
confidence and a sort of acquaintance with the truth, though they
were never quite on first name terms.
 Leading the Brexit campaign, his unique and peculiar attributes
enabled him to emerge like an English William Jennings Bryan.
Indeed, he has been the most sedulous fly catcher in recent
history, but his quarry was *Homo neanderthalensis*. Wherever
the bilge of nostalgia and vain hope ran in the veins, he set his
traps. Inside Westminster, his attributes were less desirable. It's
the misprision thing.
I should point out that Boris never intends to lie or conceal. It is
involuntary and he can no more help it than he can help

breathing. This eventually became a handicap, as, unfortunately, Boris lies very badly.
Petronella Wyatt - who knows of what she speaks

On the Origin of Species was also published as The Preservation of Favoured Races in the Struggle for Life

Omnium consensu capax imperil, nisi imperasset.
Everyone thought he would be capable of governing, until he did it.
Tacitus on Emperor Galba.

It's been about five years since I first read this, on the English language's completely universal but totally invisible adjective hierarchy, and I can honestly say I've thought about it most days since. Adjectives in English absolutely have to be in this order: opinion-size-age-shape-colour-origin-material-purpose Noun. So you can have a lovely little old rectangular green French silver whittling knife. But if you mess with that word order in the slightest you'll sound like a maniac. It's an odd thing that every English speaker uses that list, but almost none of us could write it out. And as size comes before colour, green great dragons can't exist.
Mark Forsyth: The Elements of Eloquence: How to Turn the Perfect English Phrase

Where you have a concentration of power in a few hands, all too frequently men with the mentality of gangsters get control.
Lord Acton

This is from An Immense World by Ed Yong - about how animals sense the world. A dog's world of smell is a wondrous thing....
Take a deep breath, both as demonstration and to gird yourself for some necessary terminology. When you inhale, you create a single airstream that allows you to both smell and breathe. But when a dog sniffs, structures within its nose split that airstream in two. Most of the air heads down into the lungs, but a smaller tributary, which is for smell and smell alone, zooms to the back

of the snout. There it enters a labyrinth of thin, bony walls that are plastered with a sticky sheet called the olfactory epithelium. This is where smells are first detected.

The epithelium is full of long neurons. One end of each neuron is exposed to the incoming airstream and snags passing odorants using specially shaped proteins called odorant receptors. The other end is plugged directly into a part of the brain called the olfactory bulb. When the odorant receptors successfully grab their targets, the neurons notify the brain, and the dog perceives a smell.

You can breathe out now. Humans share the same basic machinery, but dogs just have more of everything: a more extensive olfactory epithelium, dozens of times more neurons in that epithelium, almost twice as many kinds of olfactory receptors, and a relatively larger olfactory bulb. And their hardware is packed off into a separate compartment, while ours is exposed to the main flow of air through our noses. This difference is crucial. It means that whenever we exhale, we purge the odorants from our noses, causing our experience of smell to strobe and flicker. Dogs, by contrast, get a smoother experience, because odorants that enter their noses tend to stay there, and are merely replenished by every sniff.

The shape of their nostrils adds to this effect. If a dog is sniffing a patch of ground, you might imagine that every exhalation would blow odorants on the surface away from the nose. But that's not what happens. The next time you look at a dog's nose, notice that the front-facing holes taper off into side-facing slits. When the animal exhales while sniffing, air exits through those slits and creates rotating vortices that waft fresh odors into the nose. Even when breathing out, a dog is still sucking air in. In one experiment, an English pointer (who was curiously named Sir Satan) created an uninterrupted inward airstream for 40 seconds, despite exhaling 30 times during that period.

Patiently endured so long as it seemed beyond redress, a grievance comes to appear intolerable once the possibility of removing it crosses men's minds. For the mere fact that certain

abuses have been remedied draws attention to others, and they now appear more galling; people may suffer less, but their sensibility is exacerbated.
Alexis de Tocqueville

A lawyer is a person who writes a 10,000-word document and calls it a brief.
Franz Kafka

We live in a world ruled by fictions of every kind — mass merchandising, advertising, politics conducted as a branch of advertising, the instant translation of science and technology into popular imagery, the increasing blurring and intermingling of identities within the realm of consumer goods, the preempting of any free or original imaginative response to experience by the television screen. We live inside an enormous novel. For the writer in particular it is less and less necessary for him to invent the fictional content of his novel. The fiction is already there. The writer's task is to invent the reality.
JG Ballard 1973

This is from Adam Nicolson's A Seabird's Cry on the ocean world as perceived by pelagic birds
What may be featureless to us, a waste of undifferentiated ocean, is for them rich with distinction and variety, a fissured and wrinkled landscape, dense in patches, thin in others, a rolling olfactory prairie of the desired and the desirable, mottled and unreliable, speckled with life, streaky with pleasures and dangers, marbled and flecked, its riches often hidden and always mobile, but filled with places that are pregnant with life and possibility.

Is it a fact – or have I dreamed it – that, by means of electricity, the world of matter has become a great nerve, vibrating thousands of miles in a breathless point of time? Rather, the round globe is a vast head, a brain, instinct with intelligence!
Nathaniel Hawthorne 1851. What an extraordinarily perceptive vision….

26

No one worth possessing can be quite possessed.
Sara Teasdale

I cannot help but feel ambivalent at the prospect of this brave new world, in which I will be a small part of a symbiotic organism that I can barely comprehend. But then, I am a product of another kind of society, one that celebrates the individual. My sense of identity, my very sense of survival, is based on a resistance to becoming something else. Just as one of my hunting-gathering ancestors would surely reject my modern city life, so do I feel myself rebelling at this metamorphosis. This is natural. I imagine that caterpillars are skeptical of butterflies. As frightened as I am by the prospect of this change, I am also thrilled by it. I love what we are, yet I cannot help but hope that we are capable of turning into something better. We humans can be selfish, foolish, shortsighted, even cruel. Just as I can imagine these weaknesses as vestiges of our (almost) discarded animal past, I can imagine our best traits – our kindness, our creativity, our capacity to love – as hints of our future. This is the basis for my hope. I know I am a relic. I am a pre-symbiotic kind of person, born during the time of our transition. Yet, I feel lucky to have been given a glimpse of our promise. I am overwhelmed when I think of it ... by the sweet sad love of what we were, and by the frightening beauty of what we might become.
Danny Hillis: A time of transition. An essay on our movement towards a different form of human being.

There were no negative bond yields in 5,000 years of recorded history.
Richard Sylla: The History of Interest Rates

Values have become a diplomatic tool, they've been weaponised. The invocation of these values, as a result, forbids us from speaking to others. Because if you truly have values, you believe they're superior to others or even the only true ones. So when you erect values as the ultimate diplomatic tool, in fact you de facto forbid yourself from speaking to others because they do

not share your values. You build two different worlds and it's very difficult to establish a dialogue. The invocation of values is often either an admission of one's powerlessness or, on the contrary, an ambition to dominate others.
Jean de Gliniasty, French Ambassador to Russia 2009-2013

From Plato through Kant and Kohlberg, many rationalists have asserted that the ability to reason well about ethical issues causes good behaviour. They believe that reasoning is the royal road to moral truth, and they believe that people who reason well are more likely to act morally. But if that were the case, then moral philosophers—who reason about ethical principles all day long—should be more virtuous than other people. Are they?

The philosopher Eric Schwitzgebel tried to find out. He used surveys and more surreptitious methods to measure how often moral philosophers give to charity, vote, call their mothers, donate blood, donate organs, clean up after themselves at philosophy conferences, and respond to emails purportedly from students. And in none of these ways are moral philosophers better than other philosophers or professors in other fields. Schwitzgebel even scrounged up the missing-book lists from dozens of libraries libraries and found that academic books on ethics, which are presumably borrowed mostly by ethicists, are more likely to be stolen or just never returned than books in other areas of philosophy. In other words, expertise in moral reasoning does not seem to improve moral behaviour, and it might even make it worse (perhaps by making the rider more skilled at post hoc justification). Schwitzgebel still has yet to find a single measure on which moral philosophers behave better than other philosophers.

Anyone who values truth should stop worshipping reason. We all need to take a cold hard look at the evidence and see reasoning for what it is. The French cognitive scientists Hugo Mercier and Dan Sperber recently reviewed the vast research literature on motivated reasoning (in social psychology) and on the biases and errors of reasoning (in cognitive psychology). They concluded that most of the bizarre and depressing research findings make perfect sense once you see reasoning as having evolved not to help us find truth but to help us engage in arguments, persuasion, and manipulation in the context of discussions with other people. As they put it, "skilled arguers … are not after the truth but after arguments supporting their views."This explains why the confirmation bias is so powerful, and so ineradicable. How hard could it be to teach students to look on the other side, to look for evidence against their favoured view? Yet, in fact, it's very hard, and nobody has yet found a way to do it. It's hard because the confirmation bias is a built-in feature (of an argumentative mind), not a bug that can be removed (from a platonic mind).

Johnathan Haidt. The Righteous Mind: why good people are divided by politics and religion

Taiwan and China are both key to semiconductor-supply chains. Semiconductor-supply chains have multiple potential points of failure, which increase risk during times of geopolitical tensions. The production of a single chip has roughly 1,200 steps with a six-to-eight-week production cycle that is spread between countries. A Global Semiconductor Alliance analysis concludes that chip components travel more than 50,000 kilometres and cross 70 national borders before ending up at the consumption site.

What could possibly go wrong?

'Team Truss 'really does sound like the desperate finale to a BDSM orgy.

David Aronovich

Middlebrow: the point at which the principles of art meet the imperatives of the mass market.

James Marriott

Your beliefs do not make something true.

Judge Maya Guerra Gamble to the conspiracist Alex Jones when she landed him with a $45.2m fine.

Never write a letter to your mistress and never join the Carlton Club.
The Duke of Wellington

What is freedom of expression? Without the freedom to offend, it ceases to exist.
Salman Rhushdie

Don't knock threesomes. Having a threesome is like hiring an intern to do all the jobs you hate.
Sophie Ducker at the Edinburgh Fringe

You always own the option of having no opinion. There is never any need to get worked up or to trouble your soul about things you can't control. These things are not asking to be judged by you. Leave them alone.
Marcus Aurelius

I want to know God's thoughts; the rest is details.
Albert Einstein

If nobody ever said anything unless he knew what he was talking about, a ghastly hush would descend upon the earth.
Alan Herbert

Inflation consists of subsidising expenditures that give no return with the money that does not exist.
Jacques Rueff

You are so brave and quiet I forgot you are suffering.
Hemingway

Two Chelsea Pensioners sitting on a bench.
"Do you remember those pills they gave us during the war to stop us wanting women?
I think they're beginning to work."

There was a young man from Peru
Whose limericks stopped at line two
Giles Brandreth

Be yourself. Everyone else is taken.
John Lennon

There is a lot of ruin in a nation.
Adam Smith

It's best to read the weather forecast before praying for rain.
Mark Twain

A truth spoken before its time is dangerous.
Greek Proverb

31

It came out of the future which didn't exist yet, into the present that had no duration, and went into the past which had ceased to exist. I don't know that we can understand time any better than a child.
St. Augustine, when asked where time came from.

"One question remains," a German writer remarked. "What was it actually that drove us to follow [Hitler] into the abyss like the children in the story of the Pied Piper? The puzzle is not Adolf Hitler. We are the puzzle."
Ian Kershaw

I have discovered the art of deceiving diplomats. I speak the truth, and they never believe me.
Cavour

The great tragedies of history occur not when right confronts wrong but when two rights confront each other.
Henry Kissinger

Nothing is as dangerous for the state as those who would govern kingdoms with maxims found in books.
Cardinal Richelieu

SUDDENLY IT'S CLEAR WHY I WANTED TO BE OLD
Garrison Keillor
THE STORYTELLER
September 28, 2022

I look at the Great Milky Way
While inhaling the autumn bouquet
At eventide
And am mystified
And simply don't know what to say.

I love this September chill in the air. I love sweaters. They hide the age wrinkles on my inner upper arms. A stocking cap means I don't have to comb my hair. Delicate souls are yearning for Florida and maybe catch a temp job as a consumer influence consultant, enough to pay for a condo with a pool, but not me. I'm not into influence and Florida brings out the bad taste in people, and nobody wants to see an old man in a thong bikini. So here I am. I like the coffee here. I've figured out how the shower works and no longer stand under scalding water because I turned the wrong knob. I don't want to go to Florida and stay in a motel with a crank for a shower knob and be burned alive while naked. So I'll stay up north. Here I take a shower, wrap a towel around me, walk into the bedroom and sing, "O my love, my darling, I hunger for your touch." In Florida, I'd go to the ER.

The air is golden, smelling of wine and apples and woodsmoke. It takes me back to when I was 15, sitting in the press box and covering the football games for the Anoka Herald, my first paid writing job. And when I was 18, and a girl and I lay in a pile of leaves and made free with each other. Now I'm 80, the sky so clear I can see vast constellations, standing in the yard, aware of the universe and also smelling the rich spongy earth below my feet. An eternity of stars above, including stars that no longer exist, but their light still comes to us, and I stand here in mystification, having unlearned so much of what I thought I knew about life, achieving this plain peasant life. It's a second childhood. Someone told me the other day that 'racecar 'spelled backward is 'racecar'. Amazing. This is why I quit drinking and got my mitral valve replaced, so I could see beyond the average life expectancy and it's quite worth the wait, to live in a state of wonder.

"If my essays were as good as their cucumbers and lettuce, I'd be a major success, but frankly, I like being a struggling octogenarian up-and-comer"

Writing prose is a form of gardening, which my dad was good at, especially strawberries and asparagus and tomatoes. Store-bought tomatoes tasted like cardboard to him. (Now they taste the same to me.) My aunts Josephine and Eleanor were passionate gardeners. If my essays were as good as their cucumbers and lettuce, I'd be a major success, but frankly, I like being a struggling octogenarian up-and-comer. People show me deference because I walk with a cane, and that's okay, but I live in a very small world. My heroes are dead, my ambition is quite awake, I don't believe in tragedy anymore, I believe in mystery. I am mystified by my grandson and what an excellent human being he has become. He is a bulwark and an inspiration. I had two grandsons, but the other one took his own life one afternoon after school. He was a lively inquisitive boy in love with all of nature, especially animals, and had the ability to retain practically everything he ever read, and he's been gone for five years and I haven't accepted his death. I will always be mystified by it, as I am by my childhood friend Corinne, who paddled a canoe out onto Lake Cayuga one moonlit night in 1986, her pockets full of rocks, and overturned it and drowned.

It was 36 years ago, but still vivid to me, especially tonight. Memory is tied to smell and on a September night, chapters of life return to mind, unbidden. I've forgotten most of the books I ever read. Theology is of no use to me. I'm a child; I believe, 'All things work together for good to them that love God'. As a boy I used outhouses and now I walk into a men's toilet and pee in a urinal and step back and it automatically flushes. I walk around with a device in my pocket the size of a half-slice of bread and I can call my grandson for a report on Gen Z or read the Times or do a search for 'Success is counted sweetest by those who ne'er succeed. To comprehend a nectar requires sorest need'. It's a sweet world. My beloved sent me out for a walk and here I am, going nowhere, looking at everything all at once.

Queue is such a great word. The actual important letter, and then four more, silently waiting behind it in line.
Ben Rathe

You recognise a true friend by how he lies to you.
Alessandro Morandotti

Now, now my good man, this is no time for making enemies.
Voltaire, on his deathbed in response to a priest asking that he renounce Satan

I grow little of the food I eat, and of the little I do grow I did not breed or perfect the seeds.
I do not make any of my own clothing.
I speak a language I did not invent or refine.
I did not discover the mathematics I use.
I am protected by freedoms and laws I did not conceive of or legislate, and do not enforce or adjudicate.
I am moved by music I did not create myself.
When I needed medical attention, I was helpless to help myself survive.
I did not invent the transistor, the microprocessor, object oriented programming, or most of the technology I work with.
I love and admire my species, living and dead, and am totally dependent on them for my life and well being.
Steve Jobs

The man who will use his skill and constructive imagination to see how much he can give for a dollar, instead of how little he can give for a dollar, is bound to succeed.
Henry Ford

I never know whether to pity or congratulate a man on coming to his senses.
Thackeray

Cats have no need of philosophy. Obeying their nature, they are content with the life it gives them. In humans, on the other hand, discontent with their nature seems to be natural. With predictably tragic and farcical results, the human animal never ceases striving to be something that it is not. Cats make no such effort. Much of human life is a struggle for happiness. Among cats, on the other hand, happiness is the state to which they default when practical threats to their well-being are removed. That may be the chief reason many of us love cats. They possess

as their birthright a felicity humans regularly fail to attain. The source of philosophy is anxiety, and cats do not suffer from anxiety unless they are threatened or find themselves in a strange place. For humans, the world itself is a threatening and strange place. Religions are attempts to make an inhuman universe humanly habitable. Philosophers have often dismissed these faiths as being far beneath their own metaphysical speculations, but religion and philosophy serve the same need. Both try to fend off the abiding disquiet that goes with being human. Simple-minded folk will say the reason cats do not practise philosophy is that they lack the capacity for abstract thought. But one can imagine a feline species that had this ability while still retaining the ease with which they inhabit the world. If these cats turned to philosophy, it would be as an amusing branch of fantastic fiction. Rather than looking to it as a remedy for anxiety, these feline philosophers would engage in it as a kind of play.
John Gray. Feline Philosophy

I am trying to make, before I get through, a picture of the whole world—or as much of it as I have seen. Boiling it down always, rather than spreading it out thin.
Ernest Hemingway

The moral of the story? Don't take on tofu: the curds always have their whey.
David Mutterings on Twitter

The problem with the UK Tory party is not the personal defects of the captain. The problem is that you're not eligible for the captaincy unless you agree it was a brilliant idea to scupper the ship in 2016 — and can convincingly act baffled why it has been sinking ever since.
David Frum - American commentator

When I play with my cat, how do I know she is not passing time with me rather than I with her?
Montaigne

Should science by some miracle forge into the future it will come cover not only new laws of nature but new natures to have laws about… Some of the difficulty with quantum mechanics has to reside in the problem of coming to terms with the simple fact that there is no such thing as information in and of itself independent of the apparatus necessary to its perception. There were no starry skies prior to the first sentient and ocular being to behold them. Before that all was blackness and silence.
Cormac McCarthy: The Passenger

Be wiser than other people if you can; but do not tell them so.
Lord Chesterfield

The thing about Margaret's cabinet is that it includes more old Estonians than old Etonians.
Harold Macmillan

Perhaps, in the case of our new Hindu prime minister, there is something about conservatism's relationship with churchgoing, in which it's definitely good to have a faith but definitely bad to bang on about it.
Hugo Rifkind

This would be really interesting shit - if I wasn't right in the middle of it.
Barack Obama during the 2008 financial crisis

A guest sees more in an hour than the host in a year.
Polish Proverb

The intuitive mind is a sacred gift and the rational mind is a faithful servant. We have created a society that honours the servant and has forgotten the gift.
Albert Einstein

I'm afraid we still cling with part of our minds to the infantile belief that the world was made for our gratification and pleasure and we combine this narcissism with an assumption of our own

immortality. We believe that someone else will clear up the mess because that is what someone else has always done.
Boris Johnson, talking about climate change - not himself.

I'd put my money on solar energy...I hope we don't have to wait until oil and coal run out before we tackle that.
Thomas Edison, 1931

A Blairite, a Brownite, a Milibandite and a Corbynite walk into a bar. "Hello Andy Burnham," says the barman.

If I wasn't beautiful, do you think he'd be with me?
Melania Trump, when asked if she would be with her husband if he wasn't rich.

The story of his life that emerges from viewing his work chronologically is an artist of limited curiosity. Women he paints are nameless lovers; his daughters, part of a tribe of carelessly fathered children, pose naked, perhaps the only way to command his attention. His gaze is penetrating yet cold.
Sitters invariably come to the great man, so chairs and sofas recur until you feel trapped in his studio. He never experiments or takes risks or evolves much in the course of a long, much feted career. You sense him growing complacent with fame, flattered by his wealthy subjects and acolytes.
Janice Turner on Lucien Freud.

Civilizations die from suicide, not by murder.
Arnold Toynbee

Money is always there, but the pockets change .
Gertrude Stein

The crisis in a young man's life comes when he half-realises that he is hopelessly overcommitted to what he is not.
Erik Erikson, Young Man Luther

The real voyage of discovery consists not in seeking new landscapes but in having new eyes.
Proust

Where so many hours have been spent in convincing myself that I am right, is there not some reason to fear I may be wrong?
Jane Austen

Printed in Great Britain
by Amazon

18060576R00031